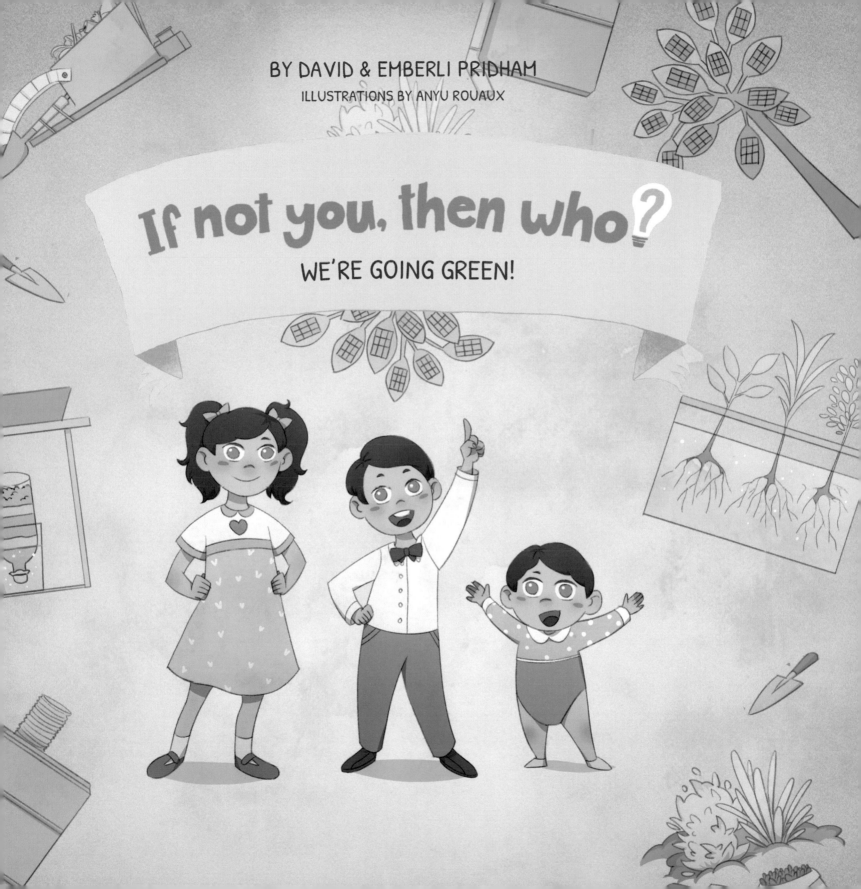

BY DAVID & EMBERLI PRIDHAM

ILLUSTRATIONS BY ANYU ROUAUX

If not you, then who?

WE'RE GOING GREEN!

If Not You, Then Who?

We're Going Green!

ISBN 978-1-951317-09-6

Published in the United States by Weeva, Inc.

First Printing, 2021

Story by David and Emberli Pridham with special assistance by Hayley Irvin of Weeva, Inc.
Creative direction by Emberli Pridham
Illustrations by Anyu Rouaux
Graphic design by Kaitlyn Tostado of Weeva, Inc.

Weeva
701 Brazos Street
Austin, TX 78735

www.weeva.com
Hello@Weeva.com

Available at bookstore.weeva.com

To this wonderful planet we all share and the children
of today who will guide its destiny!

"Of all the questions which can come before this nation, short of the actual preservation of its existence in a great war, there is none which compares in importance with the great central task of leaving this land even a better land for our descendants than it is for us."

—Theodore Roosevelt

"For, in the final analysis, our most basic common link is that we all inhabit this small planet. We all breathe the same air. We all cherish our children's future. And we are all mortal."

—John F. Kennedy

We're Going Green, the fourth book in our If Not You book series, has proven to be our most challenging endeavor to date due to the importance of the subject matter. These two quotes from Presidents Roosevelt and Kennedy exemplify the nature of this planet we share and our obligations to one another and to it. Earth is our most precious resource and what binds us all together. Our planet is in need of our help now more than ever.

It seems like every day there is news of another environmental crisis that impacts us. In our house, our children have been quick to pick up on the need for conservation and for environmental protection and restoration. Our kids are anxious to join the fight for our planet. We have often had our children approach us with creative ideas about how to, for example, help clean our oceans, protect our most endangered wildlife, improve air quality and provide clean drinking water. Its amazing to hear what they come up with.

The leaders in saving our planet will be our children and their ingenuity will help them in this task. There have been many inventions aimed at environmental conservation (for example, solar, wind and hydro power, carbon clean up and clean water) but it will be the inventions of tomorrow that help us turn the corner. That's where the inventiveness of the next generation comes into play. We know they will be up to the task.

Emberli & David Pridham

Noah felt like a small fish in a big ocean. He was at the Inventor's Fair, a big event for kids with big ideas about a big problem: protecting the environment. It was kind of a big deal. And today Noah was presenting his invention to the crowd.

Noah loved his invention. He'd spent so many weekends researching and building instead of playing. He'd emptied most of his piggy bank buying supplies instead of candy.

Noah wanted to make a difference in the world, and this was his chance.

Dad always said, "No dream is too big and no dreamer too small to make a difference." But could he? With just one small invention?

As a crowd gathered around the stage, Noah's stomach squirmed. Was it doubt or excitement? He couldn't tell. At least he didn't have to go first!

Leila, his friend from the Inventor's Club, was the first to speak. As she walked out on stage, she paused, took a deep breath, and began...

How to Make Clean Energy by Leila Tanaka

Energy is an important part of our daily lives. It's used to power buildings, cars, computers—you name it! Some types of energy can harm the environment, so scientists are looking for new ways to create clean energy.

You should know...

Clean energy comes from renewable sources like sunlight, wind, and waves.

- Clean energy does not give off greenhouse gases, also called GHGs. GHGs trap heat by letting sunlight into the atmosphere and not letting it out.

- Non-renewable energy comes from burning fuels like coal, oil, and natural gas. These are also known as fossil fuels because they are created from the remains of plants and animals buried deep in the ground.

- Fossil fuels give off GHGs when they are used.

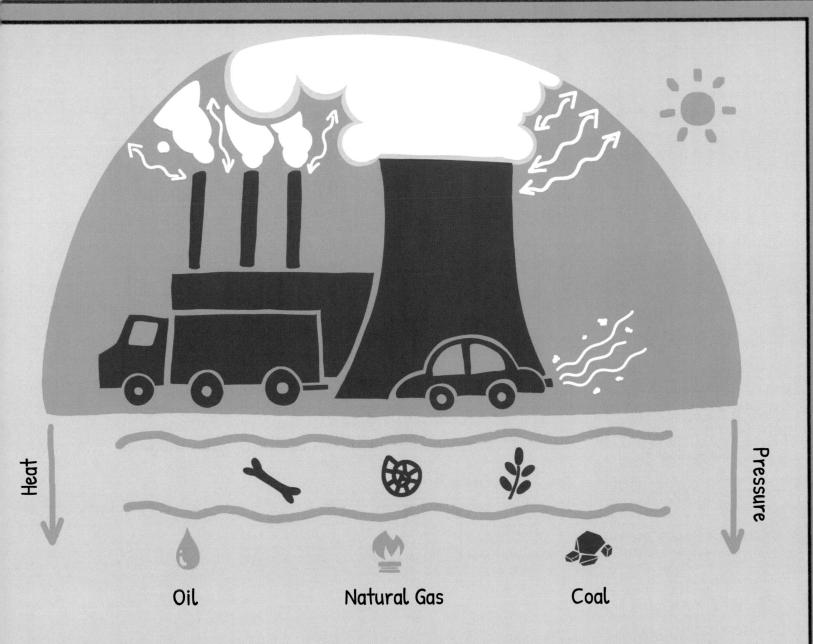

Heat

Pressure

Oil

Natural Gas

Coal

GHGs naturally occur in some amounts. But when there are too many GHGs, too much heat gets trapped and the Earth gets hotter. This could cause harmful changes to wildlife and habitats all over the world.

To protect the Earth and all of its creatures, we need to find new ways to make clean energy.

One way to capture clean energy is a solar tree. Solar trees look like real trees, but instead of leaves on the branches, there are solar panels.

Each solar panel has its own branch, and the panels move so they always face the sun. This allows them to absorb as much energy as possible every day.

Wires run through the branches and down the trunk and connect to a battery at the base of the tree. The battery stores power for later.

"Woah," thought Noah. "solar panels are so cool!"

Suddenly inspiration hit...He could use solar panels to power his invention!

Up next was Carver, who Noah remembered from summer camp. With a big, confident smile, Carver began...

Save the Bugs by Carver Lewis

30,000 species of animals face extinction every year. It's not just tigers and elephants in far away places—local wildlife is in danger too! Fortunately, there are many ways to protect local wildlife.

A big part of local wildlife that is often overlooked is insects, who play a big part in even the smallest of ecosystems.

An ecosystem is a group of living things that live and work together in one place. Ecosystems are everywhere, even our own backyards!

Insects are an important part of a healthy ecosystem because...

- They keep the soil healthy.

- They help pollinate plants.

- They are food for small animals like birds and lizards, who are food for bigger animals.

hawk eats frog

An ecosystem would fall apart without insects. Plants would stop growing and animals wouldn't have enough food. If we want to save wildlife, we can start with the bugs in our backyards.

frog eats worm

worms help soil

plants grow

Butterfly gardens are a great way to help local insects, but it's important to plant the right flowers. My butterfly garden kit has the right seeds to start a butterfly garden here in our neighborhood.

Butterflies need host plants and nectar plants.

Host plants are food and shelter for butterfly eggs and caterpillars. Our local butterflies like milkweed and passionflower.

Nectar plants are food for adult butterflies. Our local butterflies like to eat goldenrods and Texas star hibiscus.

With my butterfly garden kit, anyone can help protect local wildlife!

Milkweed

Passionflower

SEEDS

Texas Star Hibiscus

Goldenrod

Woah, Carver made it look so easy! He had clearly spent a lot of time studying and could answer everyone's questions with ease.

Noah thought of all the games of dancing bean bag golf he'd missed, but right now it made him feel so much better to know he'd prepared.

There was now only one person before Noah: his friend Emily, who lived down the street. She looked so excited as she began her presentation.

Conserving Water by Emily Hopper

Water is a vital part of life, but in some places, humans are using water faster than it can be renewed. To make sure we have plenty of water to use in the future, scientist are looking for new ways to conserve water today.

Did you know that...?

1 It takes 1 gallon of water to grow a single almond, and 13 gallons to grow an orange!

2 An 8-minute shower uses 17 gallons of water!

3 Farming uses even more than that! 80% of water used every year is used to grow crops.

4 Humans use roughly 300 gallons of water at home every day. 210 gallons are used for indoor uses like cooking and cleaning. 90 gallons are used for outdoor activities like gardening.

If we can conserve water in every one of these areas, we'll be well on our way to saving water for future generations.

For my project, I built a device to collect and purify rainwater. Water is first collected in a big tank at the top of the container. Then the water runs through four filters.

The first filter is rocks. These rocks will catch any large twigs or leaves that might get into the tank.

The second filter is charcoal. It helps clean and purify the water. Then the water is drained through fine sand to remove any remaining impurities.

Finally, clean water drips through a cheese cloth and into a container.

Once the water has been purified, it can be used to help water plants.

Woah...we could run out of clean water? Noah had never thought about it before, and he was worried.

No wonder Emily was eager to share her invention! Noah made a mental note to take shorter showers.

At last it was Noah's turn! Confident and prepared, he jumped onto the stage, took a deep breath, and smiled.

Cleaning Our Oceans by Noah Fairley

Oceans are an important resource on our planet. However, plastic pollution is a great threat to our oceans and the wildlife that lives there.

Did you know that...?

1 Over 20,000 species of animals live in our oceans. That's 3.5 TRILLION fish!

2 A system of currents flows through every ocean in the world and connects them together like an underwater highway. Fish aren't the only travelers on these highways—litter can cruise on them too!

3 14 billion pounds of trash are dumped into the oceans every year.

After trash enters the ocean, it washes up on shore or travels along the currents. If the trash travels far enough, it will reach the Great Pacific Garbage Patch. Most of this trash is plastic waste like bottles and bags.

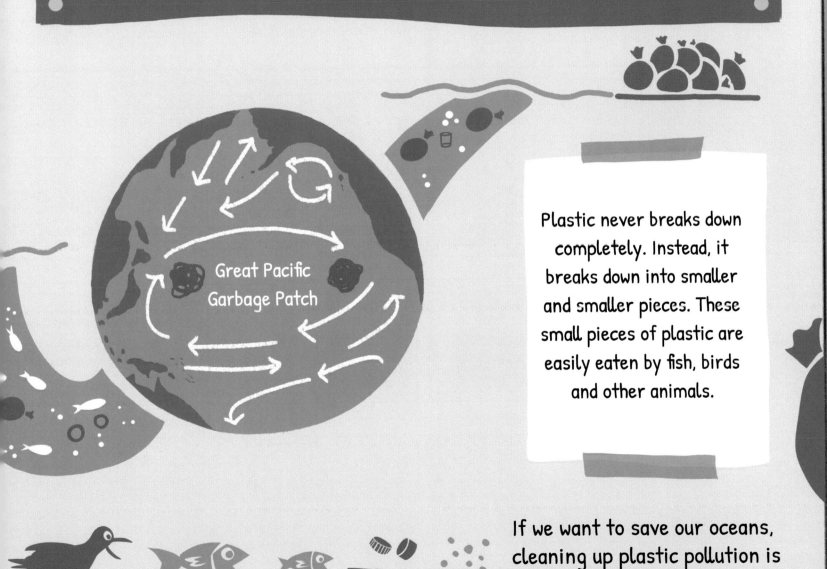

Great Pacific Garbage Patch

Plastic never breaks down completely. Instead, it breaks down into smaller and smaller pieces. These small pieces of plastic are easily eaten by fish, birds and other animals.

If we want to save our oceans, cleaning up plastic pollution is a great place to start.

For my project, I built a device to collect plastic and other litter from the ocean.

The device is powered by a motor and driven with a remote control.

The scoop picks up the litter and then drops it into a container at the back of the device.

Once the container is full, bring the boat back to the shore, empty it, and go again. Make sure to recycle what you collect!

"**Woah, Woah Noah!**" said Brooke. "You know your stuff!"

"That's our boy!" cheered Mom and Dad.

"Bravo!" added Grandpa.

"Go, Nobee!" said Graham.

After all the presentations were finished, Dr. Morales and Professor Wetzel, the teachers for the Inventor's Club, came to inspect his invention.

"What a great idea, Noah! We could use your invention to help clean up the local pond," said Professor Wetzel.

"And we'll ask the school to only use paper straws from now on!" added Dr. Morales.

"Woah" thought Noah. "Did I just make a difference?"

As they were walking home, Dad announced, "You know what? I've decided we're going to put solar panels on our roof! It's about time our house ran on clean energy."

"And I want to start a garden in the backyard so all the birds and bugs are happy and healthy!" Brooke chimed in.

"Great idea!" Mom said. "And maybe we can find ways
to conserve water, too?"

"I know!" Noah said. "We can collect rainwater for
the garden!"

"Feed birdies!" shouted baby Graham. Even Noah's
little brother was inspired.

What can you do to go green at home?

The next week was a busy one.

Little changes were happening everywhere around the house, and the paper straws had already shown up at school.

When Noah looked at his invention, he marveled. Dad was right after all. His dreams weren't too big and he wasn't too small. He hadn't built a big machine or cleaned an entire ocean, but he had made a difference.

And he couldn't wait to do it again tomorrow.

FRIENDS OF OUR PLANET

SIERRA
CLUB

TAKE ACTION!

Are you looking for more ways to Go Green? Join with our fabulous partners and learn more ways to help Planet Earth.

The Sierra Club for Kids

The Sierra Club for Kids is the most enduring and influential grassroots environmental organization in the United States. We amplify the power of our 3.8 million members and supporters to defend everyone's right to a healthy world.

Kids for Saving the Earth

Kids for Saving Earth is a nonprofit organization created to educate and empower children to help protect Earth. Environmental education materials and website are designed to provide instructors with easy ways to add education into action curriculum to their learning environment.

Earth Force

Earth Force engages young people as active citizens who improve the environment and their communities now and in the future. We envision a world where everyone has the knowledge and skills they need to participate in environmental decision making in their community.

WANT TO LEARN MORE?

If you feel inspired by the inventions in this book and want to know more about the inventions and young inventors that inspired them, go to **IfNotYouBooks.com/Green**

LEILA'S SOLAR TREE

NOAH'S LITTER COLLECTOR

EMILY'S WATER PURIFIER

CARVER'S BUTTERFLY GARDEN

IF YOU LIKED LEARNING ABOUT GOING GREEN AND WANT TO GO ON MORE
ADVENTURES WITH BROOKE, NOAH, AND BABY GRAHAM, CHECK OUT
THESE OTHER TITLES FROM THE IF NOT YOU, THEN WHO? SERIES:

Join our mailing list at **IfNotYouBooks.com** to be the first to know about new releases and special promotions, and be sure to leave a review for other young inventors!

We can't wait to hear from you!

David & Emberli

the Young Inventor's Club

The Young Inventors Club celebrates inventors and their extraordinary achievements—and starts your child on a journey of fun, adventure, and creativity! As a club member, you'll help your child learn about patents, inventors, past inventions, and how to come up with inventions of their own. We will send you monthly hands-on STEM activities to engage curious kids in the world around them. You can submit completed challenges for chances to win exclusive prizes every month.

Joining is FREE!

www.ifnotyoubooks.com/inventors-club/

David and Emberli Pridham make their homes between Dallas, Texas and Barrington, Rhode Island along with their children Brooke, Noah, and Graham and their cat, Miss Beasley. David is the CEO of Dominion Harbor Enterprises, a patent transactional firm based in Dallas, Texas.

MADE WITH LOVE IN TEXAS

Printed in the USA